The Shark with no teeth

Written and illustrated
by
Shoo Rayner

D0488698

We all know that sharks have lots of
big teeth. Well, this is a story about
a shark that lost his teeth.
The shark was called Cruncher.

Before Cruncher lost his teeth
he could eat anything he liked.
Best of all he liked to eat things with
shells because they went CRUNCH.
All the other animals in the sea were
scared of him.
But then one day something happened.

Cruncher saw a giant turtle
swimming by.
'I will eat that turtle for my tea,'
said Cruncher.
When the turtle saw Cruncher he hid
inside his shell. Cruncher opened his
mouth as far as it would go. CRUNCH!
The turtle's shell was too hard and
all of Cruncher's teeth fell out.

From that day on, all Cruncher could eat was jellyfish and sponges.
The other animals in the sea were not scared of him any more.

All the other sharks laughed at
Cruncher. They swam by him
and smiled and showed him their
big teeth.
'Look at that shark with no teeth,'
they would say.

'I'll show them,' said Cruncher.
'I may not have teeth, but I can still
scare all the animals in the sea.'
So Cruncher swam off looking for
someone to scare.

First of all Cruncher saw a little crab.
He called out to the crab,

'You don't scare me,' said the crab.
'You haven't got any teeth.'
Then the crab walked up to Cruncher
and hit him on the nose.
Cruncher was cross. He wanted to eat
the crab and crunch its shell.
But Cruncher had no teeth.

So Cruncher swam away.

Next he saw a little lobster.

He called out to the lobster,

Look out little lobster,
look out for me.
I'm Cruncher the shark,
and I'll eat you for tea.

'You don't scare me,' said the lobster.
'You haven't got any teeth.'
Then the lobster swam up to Cruncher
and gave him a nip with his claw.
Cruncher was cross. He wanted to eat
the lobster and crunch its shell.
But Cruncher had no teeth.

So Cruncher swam away.

Then he saw a little swordfish.

He called out to the swordfish,

Look out little swordfish,
look out for me.
I'm Cruncher the shark,
and I'll eat you for tea.

'You don't scare me,' said the
swordfish. 'You haven't got any teeth.'
Then the swordfish swam up to
Cruncher and pushed him in the
tummy with his big, long nose.

By now, Cruncher was very sad.
No one was scared of him any more
and he couldn't eat the food he liked
best. When the other sharks saw
how sad Cruncher was they stopped
laughing at him.
'I know what we can do,' said one
shark, and she swam off as fast as
she could.

The next day the shark gave Cruncher
a present. She had made him a new set
of teeth out of sea shells.
Cruncher was very happy.
'I have teeth again,' he shouted.
'Oh, thank you, thank you.'
And off he swam.

The next day the crab, the lobster and
the swordfish saw Cruncher again.
'We're not scared of you,' they said.

Then Cruncher smiled ...